Screech.

It is raining and
the road is very wet.

2

A car stops —
SCREECH!

A truck stops —
SCREECH!

A motorbike stops —

SCREECH!

A bus stops —
SCREECH!

Why is all the traffic
stopping?

The ducks are crossing
the road.
Quick! Quick! Quick!
Quack! Quack! Quack!

8